The Spirit of Christmas
at Notre Dame

The Spirit of Christmas
at Notre Dame

Susan Mullen Guibert
and
Brendan O'Shaughnessy

Illustrated
by
Nicholas Gunty

Corby Books
A Division of Corby Publications
Notre Dame, Indiana

The Spirit of Christmas at Notre Dame

10 9 8 7 6 5 4 3 2

ISBN 987 978-09912451-6-1
Manufactured in the United States of America

Published by Corby Books
A Division of Corby Publishing, LP
P.O. Box 93
Notre Dame, Indiana 46556
www.corbypublishing.com

"It is my prayer that the whole Notre Dame family will be able to reconnect with the Christmas spirit – Christ's spirit – in times of happiness and in times of need. 'The Christmas Spirit at Notre Dame' offers a glimpse into the uncomplicated joy of childhood and how tapping that part of the soul provides peace."

– Rev. Theodore Hesburgh, C.S.C.

'Twas the night before finals
and all through the dorm,
Not a student could study;
they were watching the storm.

4

When Grace in her parka and Kathleen in her wool
Made a trek across campus to study for school.
"I'm worried!" said Grace. "All the papers and tests!"
"Don't fret," said Kathleen. "You'll be fine. Try your best!"

5

"I long for the time when finals didn't matter...
When Christmas meant presents and cookies on platters!
All thoughts were of Rudolph, stockings and the Grinch...
Childhood without finals seemed like a cinch!"

6

The hands of the clock circled hour after hour...
Her lids grew heavy — she needed coffee or a shower.
Grace closed her eyes wishing for a bed
As physics and writers danced in her head.

7

When a jingle and a whoosh caused her to awake,
"Was that real? Was that Santa? It must be a fake!"
She ran to the window and saw what she saw!
"It is Santa!" she cried, with wonder and awe...

9

10

Grace ran down the stairs and she spied right away
On the quad sat St. Nick, eight reindeer and sleigh.
He called her to join him and take a short ride,
She approached the sleigh slowly, her eyes open wide.

11

His face looked familiar — a leader or scholar?
She jumped right inside but felt strangely quite smaller!
His magic had turned her back into a child!
"How could this be?" she asked, but Santa just smiled.

He whistled and shouted 'til away they flew
Over Dome, under moon, Santa's voice came through:
"Let's recapture warm feelings of reading and knowledge
That you felt as a kid when dreaming of college."

13

"Remember your family gathered all 'round the fire
Watching the bowl game go down to the wire.
The final big play made everyone roar
And dance 'round the tree across the wood floor."

14

"Your first trip to campus, you flocked to the ducks
That glide on the lakes, nature's bounty in flux.
Your mother broke bread for the birds to be fed
They quacked as they waddled, all moving ahead."

15

"A short walk to the Grotto   to offer a prayer
    You lit a small candle and   decided right there
To land in this place that   mix'd beauty with faith—
    A wish for your birthday,   but only your eighth."

16

"After four years went by,
 you came back for a Mass
In the Church where the sunlight
 peeked through stained glass.
It felt just like home,
 the glow of peace that you found.
It was then that you knew
 you were on holy ground."

17

"Your first time in the stadium was such a big thrill
After years of fall tailgates, huddled 'round the grill.
You were old enough then to sit with your father
And cheer for the Irish with a clap and a holler."

18

"You finally arrived as a student this fall.
There's you on the quad with your friends standing tall.
Your parents so proud that you joined their tradition
Grown to a person of faith and education."

19

20

"A child no more though the magic's still there,
Dig deep in your heart and whisper a prayer.
To believe once again, the school spirit you found
Will give your heart peace and joy will abound."

21

"Kathleen! What just happened? Did you see him too?
Hey Connor and Michael — 'twas Santa! He flew!
We all must remember, as children we knew,
The joy and the magic, the wonder anew!"

22

They gazed up in awe with the sleigh in the air
Like children they marveled and heard him declare:

23

"Bethlehem was brilliant the night of Christ's birth
But Notre Dame sparkles like no place on earth!"

24

Other Books

If you loved The Spirit of Christmas at Notre Dame, you will also enjoy the two other classic children's books by Susan M. Guibert and Brendan O'Shaughnessy: Clashmore Mike Comes Home and Clashmore Mike - Dublin to Dome.

Clashmore Mike, a spunky Irish Terrier originally given as a gift to Knute Rockne, inspired and entertained fans for more than 40 years before the leprechaun.

Notre Dame fans of all ages will enjoy the adventures of Mikey, a modern-day Irish Terrier who comes to campus for a tailgate party with his family. Mikey gets lost from his people, but through his exploration of campus, discovers the true story of Clashmore Mike.

Notre Dame's famed leprechaun wasn't the first mascot to help the team shake down the thunder. From 1924 to 1965, Clashmore Mike's antics on and off the field brought the team more than luck – the little terriers had a better record than any other mascot in college football.

In this sequel, an old terrier in the Irish village of Clashmore, Ireland, recalls how he accidentally joined a family emigrating to America in 1924 and wound up as the original mascot of Fighting Irish football.

Available at:

corbypublishing.com • Hammes Notre Dame Bookstore • amazon.com